CW00868542

Also by Cartoon Dave

Cartoon Dave's NO-RULES Cartooning
Cartoon Dave's Fab Face Freakout
M.A.D Cartooning (Monsters. Aliens. Dinosaurs)
Hands On Cartooning
UFO – Unavoidable Family Outing
UFO in the USA
UFO Afloat
Unstoppable Brainspin
Sumo Granny Smackdown
Norman Enormous
Hamilton's Handstand

Up until now, Dawko and Ditz have kept their noses out of other people's bottoms...

THE BUM BOOK

by **Dawko & Ditz**

Illustrations by CARTOON DAVE

Dawko; 1969 -
Ditz; 1964 -
Hackett, Dave; 1970 -

The Bum Book

ISBN 978-0-646-58220-7

Text copyright © 2012 by Dawko & Ditz. Illustrations copyright © 2012 Dave Hackett.

All rights reserved. No part of this book may be reproduced or transmitted in any form or by any means, electronic or mechanical, including photocopying, recording, storage, in an information retrieval system, or otherwise, without the prior written permission of the publisher, unless specifically permitted under the Australian Copyright Act 1968 as amended.

Typesetting by Dawko. Typeset in Adobe Garamond Pro 16pt.

To the Cousins family - if there is a family more tuned in to bum humour, I've yet to meet them! – **Cartoon Dave**

To all the parents, grandparents, teachers and librarians who understand the importance of children learning to master the art of reading. Keep up the good work! – **Ditz**

To Joy, Lachlan and Matthew - my personal research laboratory (a.k.a. family). Thanks for remembering my name during the long process of making this book real. – **Dawko**

CONTENTS

CONTENTS

(Continued)

CONTENTS

(Continued)

7

CONTENTS

(Continued)

The Bum Book

This

Hilariously

Engrossing

Book's

Utter

Madness

Brings

Out

Odorous

Knowledge

CRACKED FACT

What does "Odorous Knowledge" mean?
It means all the facts
and information about smells!

— Ditz

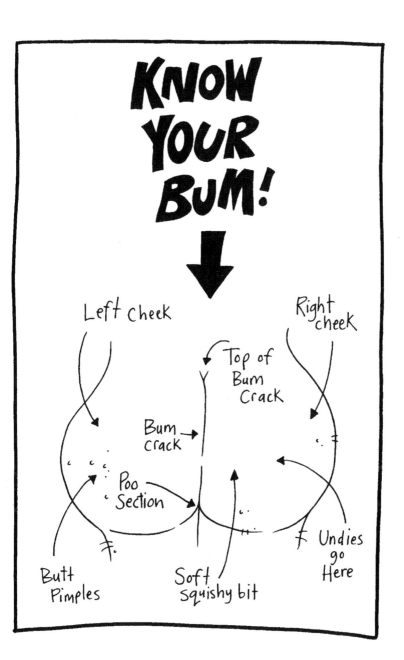

I Hate Reading!

I don't like to read, I don't think that it's cool
They make you read books
in the classroom at school
I'd rather play video games by myself
Those silly old books can   just

stay

on

the

shelf!

And anyway, no-one writes my kind of book
If they did, maybe then I would give it a look
I don't want to read about wizards or witches
Not even if those books
have lots of great pictures

I don't want to read about kids riding horses

Or wimps and their troubles,

or strange, evil forces

I don't want to read any vampire romance

I just want to read about **foul underpants**!

That's right. I admit it. It's not just a rumour

I don't like to read, but I love toilet humour

Bottoms and undies and farting and poo

Who would read that book?

Well, I would! That's who!

Looking Up Bottoms

I love my new thesaurus,
I am really very keen
I love to look up silly words,
And find out what they mean

Today I looked up **bottom**,
And I found it's called a *seat*,
But it was all the other names,
That I found really neat

It can be called a *fundament*,
A *keister, tail* or *rump,*
I think they are such funny names
To call my little bump!

Others took my fancy,

Such as *buttocks*, *rear*, and *prat*.

Hindquarters! *TUSHIE!* **DERRIÈRE!**

What do you think of that?

There are lots of names for your caboose

I've given you just some…

How many more words can you find

That all mean simply… bum?

CRACKED FACT

A Thesaurus is awesome fun for word play. If you don't have one at home (or school) you should ask for one! You'll be blown away like a fart in the wind!

- Dawko

LONG-LOST BUMS

Draw a line to match the Bums
to their owners

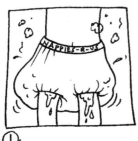

Joyce the Granny

Bruno the Plumber

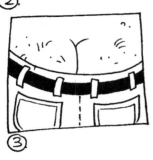

Darren the Baby

Sibling Rivalry

A little girl, whose name was Pearl
Just loved the fact she was a girl
    And so that all the world could know
She wrote a poem saying so

What is a little girl made of?

It's really plain to see

She's made of sun and flowers

There's none so sweet as me

She's made of spice and sugar

And honey on a spoon

She's pretty as a princess

And as lovely as the moon

CRACKED FACT

My sister and I used to write poems together when we were kids. We'd use tricky words so it would be very hard to rhyme! Maybe you can try it with your siblings.

- DawKo

She left the poem on her bed
Her brother read it, and he said
"What rubbish!" as he gave a smirk
Then grabbed a pen and got to work

What is a little girl made of?

It's ~~really plain~~ HORRIBLE to see

She's made of ~~sun~~ Bums and ~~flowers~~ Monkeys

And chocolate-coated Wee!

~~There's none so sweet as me~~

She's made of ~~spice~~ Mice and ~~sugar~~ Boogers

and ~~honey~~ Deadflies on a ~~spoon~~ Poo

she's ~~pretty~~ yucky as a ~~princess~~ mud pile

and as ~~lovely~~ smelly as the ~~moon~~ zoo!!

When little Pearl came back inside
She found the poem, and she cried
    "Oh, this means war! Prepare to fight!"
She sat down and began to write

What is a little boy made of?

It's difficult to bear

He's made of mouldy toe-jam

And snotty nostril hair

He's made of sweaty bum-cracks

And old undies filled with spew

He's farty as a sheep farm

And he smells like poo - times two!

She gave it to her brother then

He read it once, and once again

He turned to her, "This is," he said

"The nicest thing I've ever read!"

The Best Fart

This is the fart,

    The very best fart,

        The very best fart of them all!

Oh, it will be smelly,

From deep in my belly

And it's gonna make your skin crawl

This is the fart,

The very best fart,

The very best fart of them all!

Oh, it will be loud

It will make my dog proud

It will peel all the paint from the wall

This is the fart, the very best fart,

And it comes from my heart

And it makes your eyes smart

It tears nostrils apart

And it stings like a dart

And it soars

    off the chart

Like I said from the start

Yes this is the fart

    The very best fart,

        The very best fart of them all!

WHOSE POO?

Draw a line between each poo and the thing that may have created it...

The Bum Shop

Tomorrow we start back at school

No more TV or acting cool

But yesterday we had to go

To get our uniforms, you know

I'd grown a bit (I'm nearly 10)

And so had my big sister, Gwen

So in we went to get some socks

And shirts and skirts and shorts and jocks

I was just trying on my shorts

When I heard one of mum's dry snorts

"My goodness, Tom, my little chum,

"It seems that you've outgrown your bum."

CRACKED FACT

Did you Know that your ears and nose
Keep growing for your whole life?
Your bum will only Keep growing if you
chow down on too much fried food.

- Ditz

She dragged me out then from the shop

I squealed and tried to make her stop

We strode and strode all through the mall

Until we reached the Bottom Hall

At "Bargain Buttocks" mum slowed down

But then she checked out "Bottom Town"

Past "Cheek Boutique" we calmly strolled

And settled on "Where Bums 'R' Sold"

The shop was busy, filled with mums

Who had to buy their children bums

We looked around to find my size

But couldn't, much to my surprise

Mum dug d
o
w
n in the bargain bin

'til she had bums up to her chin

But still my size she could not find

"My goodness! Aren't we in a bind?

"I never thought the day would come,

"A mum can't buy her boy a bum!"

She grabbed her chin and made a frown,

"There's always Gwen's old hand-me-down."

I stomped my foot. "No way!" I said

"I'd rather have NO bum instead!

"I get her hats and jumpers, too,

"Just once, can't I have something new?"

"All right, young Tom, don't make a scene."

"Please listen now, mum: Gwen's fifteen,

"Her bum from last year won't be right

"In shape or size, in width or height."

Mum crossed her arms and gave a sigh

But then the back room caught her eye

The sign above said

SCRATCH & DENT

And very quickly, in mum went

She found my size and didn't care

About the patch of orange hair

That grew out of that bum's left cheek

"Oh, we can shave that once a week."

So now I'm scared to face tomorrow

My weird bum fills me with sorrow

Maybe I can take it back

'Cause after all...it has a crack!

THINGS THAT COULD BE MISTAKEN FOR BUMS

A FUZZY PEACH

SOME DUDE'S CHIN

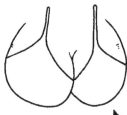

BRA-OBJECTS

ROGER, THE CAT

Disgusting Brother

My brother's a disgusting boy,

Annoying me gives him such joy

He's yucky in so many ways

He doesn't
        wash
             for
                 days
                   and
                     days

He thinks that it is just and right

To wear his undies day and night

And then he makes me scream and shout

'Cause then he turns them inside out!

He wears them once, he wears them twice

He makes them last a week – not nice!

"Saves water," he says with a grin

Until they stick onto his skin

There's nothing else that makes me yell

Quite like my yucky brother's smell

My brother makes me want to hurl

Why couldn't he have been a girl?

THINGS TO KNOW ABOUT BUMS

1. Bums stink.

2. You know at least three people who have bums.

3. Fish have bums.

4. Dogs have considerably hairier bums than fish.

5. Your teacher has a bum.

6. There is a 72 percent chance that your teacher's bum is wrinkly.

7. Bums should not be used as ironing boards.

8. You can't fold a bum in half.

9. If your bum accidentally falls off, you won't grow a new one.

10. Yes, bums have cheeks, but no — bums are not a part of your face (if in doubt, try smiling with your bum).

11. The number one ingredient in bums is meat (followed closely by blood, veins, weird tube-things and poo).

12. Bums are a cool hang-out place for flies, crawly bugs and worms.

I Did The One

I did the one

that rattled the door.

I have been practicing

since I was four.

I did the one

that coloured the curtain,

It was a mean one,

and that is for certain.

I did the one

that killed all the plants,

It was a rocket

right out of my pants,

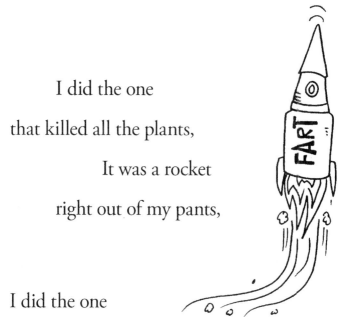

I did the one

that shook through the floor,

My Mum came and begged me,

"Please, Dawko, no more!"

I did the one

that sent my dog potty,

I made him go mad

with my super charged botty.

I did the one

that melted my sister

(Well, it didn't quite melt her,

it just made her blister)

I did the one

that made the paint peel

It hovered for ages

and made the cat squeal

I did the one

that knocked over my Gran,

It cheesed off my mum,

and so outside I ran!

Glum Bum

If I was a big boy's bum

I think that I'd be rather glum

Life, they say, is so unfair

When you're a young man's derrière

Do you know how many times a day

A boy will fart? Fourteen! No way!

A girl's bum must think it's in heaven...

Girls will only do eleven!

"So what?" you say. "Three more each day!

"Three farts won't blow a bum away!"

Well, yes, you're right, but listen here...

How
many
days
are
in
a
year?

NUMBER OF FARTS

		Girls	Boys	Difference
	Day	11	14	3
x 7	Week	77	98	21
x 28	Month	308	392	84
x 365	Year	4015	5,110	1,095
x 80	Years*	321,420	409,080	87,660

*Including Leap Years

And if you lived for 80 years

Boys, I fear for all your rears

See, all those extra farts you do

Will make the planet say "peee-yew!"

The Prime Minister may pass a law

To punish those whose bums fart more

You won't be getting bottom smacks

You'll get a bottom Carbon Tax!

Butt Name

Life can be funny, life can be great,

When your surname involves a butt,

Whenever you tell someone your name

They think that you're a nut

Buttazoni, Buttel and Bumstead,

Will get the giggles going,

Buttinski, Butters and Buttifant,

Will keep the laughter flowing!

Ramsbottom and Longbottom,

Will bring people to their knees

But I have the greatest butt name

And my school kids love to tease

You see, I am a teacher

And my name is quite a pain

My name makes people smile and laugh,

As if they're quite insane

When I walk into the classroom,

And I write upon the board

"My name is Mister Buttkiss"

Everybody sits there, floored!

CRACKED FACT

For once, we actually didn't have to be silly.
That's right — all of the surnames in this
poem are real names!

- Ditz

LET'S DRAW BUM DUDES!

It's time to pick up your pencils and find out just how simple it is to draw your own BUM DUDES!

① Grab a straight line + a 'U' shape...

② Now for the other cheek...

③ ..and this little bit too

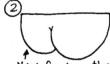

④ Simple circles and dots for eyes...

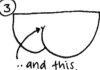

⑤ Here's a simple mouth!

⑥ Buttpimples, hairs and eyebrows, too!

⑦ Remember that the hands don't need to be too amazing — any kind of arms with a bunch of fingers will do!

⑧ start with this leg first.

The feet are long blobs with 3 'C' shapes for toes — Here's a simple foot that works too

Now it's your turn— Over the next couple of pages there's loads of space to try your own Bum Dudes — Have fun, and... happy Bums!!?
(I've included some eyes, mouths etc. for you, too!)
And if you get stuck, turn back to the page before this one! **EYES**
Good luck!!

MOUTHS

OK, now let's put it all together. Here, you get to draw a bunch of Bum Dudes, and then—you can make them say whatever you like by writing spectacular words inside the speech bubbles!

My Bum's On Strike

Last Monday I was acting cool

    Just walking with my mates to school

        We passed the station and the pool

        And cut through Macka's Field

We must have made it half way through

        When suddenly I had to poo

        I knew that there would be no loo

        I thought my fate was sealed

I found a place behind some plants

Then dug a hole and dropped my pants

Squatted down and took the stance

As easy as you like

I gave a squeeze, I gave a yell

I pushed and pushed but nothing fell

I couldn't even make a smell

My bum had gone on strike!

I threatened it with being smacked

But had to face the wacky fact

I always knew my bum was cracked

But never was it broken

I told my bum it was berserk

And asked it why it wouldn't work

But it sat back and with a smirk

It said "You must be jokin'!

"I need a very clean commode

"If I am going to drop my load,

"I won't just do it by the road,

"I really can't abide it!"

I stood and dressed and tried to run

I feared before this day was done

That my poor bum would weigh a ton

With all the poo inside it

I scampered off towards the shop

I couldn't run, but couldn't stop

Then pretty soon I had to hop

My guts were really aching

I found a public toilet block

I went inside but got a shock

It smelled like some old sweaty sock!

By now my knees were shaking

The floor was wet, the ceiling too

The walls were covered with green goo

The toilet bowl

was filled with poo

It looked

just like a mountain

The rotten flusher wouldn't flush

Of course, there was no toilet brush

But I was now in such a rush

I would have used a fountain!

But once again my bum refused

I tell you, I was not amused

I threatened it with being bruised

For treating me so meanly

"Now listen, boy," it calmly said

"This awful place fills me with dread,

"Please try to get it through your head,

"I need to do it cleanly."

So off I hobbled, wracked with pain

Bending double with the strain

I swear I thought I'd go insane

And nearly started crying

I got to class at half-past ten

Still walking like an alien

But pretty soon I left again

I thought that I was dying

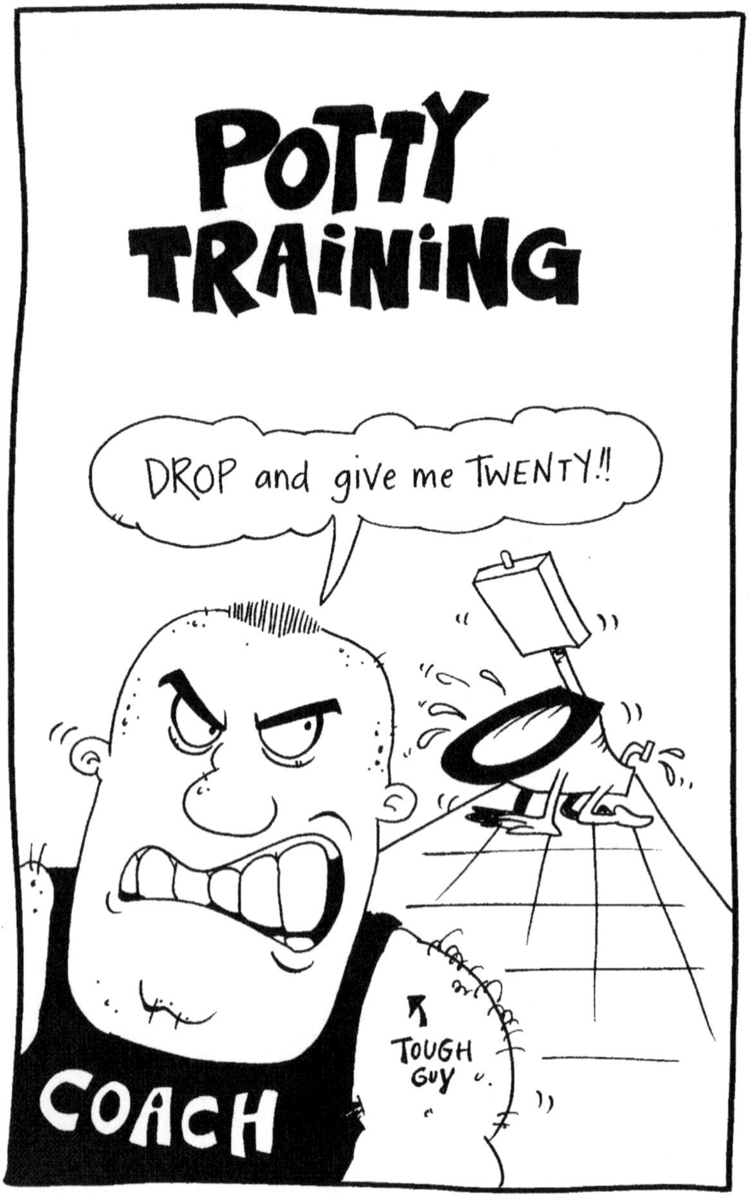
POTTY TRAINING
DROP and give me TWENTY!!
TOUGH GUY
COACH

I tottered to the toilet door

My belly gave a grumbling roar

       I fell and crawled along the floor

Knocked over by the stench

I knew that I could barely hope

That my poor fussy bum would cope

       It took one look and just said "Nope."

Then locked up in a clench

I battled on throughout the day

I felt like I was filled with clay

The bell rang! I was on my way!

And running home so quickly

Through the front door, to the loo

So clean and fresh – it smelled nice too

And finally, that stinky poo

Could pour out of me slickly!

CRACKED FACT

My children were the inspiration for this poem. Their school toilets were so awful that my girls would hold onto their poo all day, just so they could do it at home!

\- Ditz

That day my bum, it wore me out

I never knew a bum could pout

I wanted to get mad and shout:

"Hey bum – I'm going to spank you!"

Instead I turned my head around

I bent my back and shoulders down

       I faced my bum without a frown

And I said simply "Thank you".

My Poo Haiku

Have you seen my poo?

I left it here just last night

Where could it be now?

CRACKED FACT

Haiku is originally a form of Japanese poetry. The classic form of Haiku in English is to have a poem of three lines and 17 syllables, in the pattern 5, 7, 5.

— Dawko

Exploding Bums

I wish I had an exploding bum

    Like some beetles I've read about

When an enemy comes, they burst their bums

    And knock those suckers out!

Well, there's a tough kid at my school

    Who picks on me all day

There's nothing I can say or do

    To make him go away

But I wonder if he'd let me be

And just get off my case

If I dropped my pants and burst

My little bum right in his face!

D.I.Y BUM STORY

Make your own story by filling the blank spaces with words from my list— or any cool words you know!

Bum
Poo
Botty
Fart
Underpants
Wee
Toilet
Vomit
Diarrhoea
Globby
Stinky
Slimy
Nose-pick
Goat

She was the love of my life. Her name was Suzie _____.
She wore a hat made from an old _____ _____, and looked beautiful in it.

On our first date, we saw a terrifying movie called "Revenge of the killer _____."

78

I took her hand, and we built
_____ castles by the ocean.
We snacked on _____ and
_____ juice as the sun set,
and talked romantically about
_____ _____ until
dinner. At the restaurant (which
was called "La_____"), the
waiter brought us a large plate of
deliciously hot_____ _____,
which we gobbled down madly.
After our first date, we were quickly
married, and had sixteen beautiful
baby _____s, who all grew
up to look just like their mother.

The Life of a Toilet

If your toilet could talk,

just what would it say?

Would it welcome you in

with a hearty "g'day"?

I think it might scowl

and say, "Go on, shoo!"

Because it would know

what you're in there to do!

If your toilet could speak,

would it give you a name?

Could it tell us apart? Do we all look the same?

I think it might call us some names rather rude,

Let's face it, it's likely in quite a bad mood.

If your toilet had brains,

do you think it would think?

Or maybe it couldn't because of the stink.

I think it might sit there and just meditate,

And try to achieve an oblivious state.

And if your toilet could think,

would it make up ideas,

About how to avoid

all our round naked rears?

I think that it might

form a brilliant plan

To run far away,

just as fast as it can!

If your toilet could walk,

do you think it would stay?

Would it sit still and wait for you, day after day?

I think that it might

rather get up and run,

The life of a toilet

can't be too much fun.

And if it could run,

well just where would it go?

Would it sit in the sun,

or head for the snow?

I think that it might

take a long ocean cruise,

Just to get far away

from the wees and the poos!

GREETINGS FROM

SYDNEY
Harbour Bum

SYDNEY oPoora House

85

Disgusting Brother II:
Underpants Dance

My brother's a disgusting boy,

Annoying me gives him such joy

He does so many yucky things

And tells me of the glee it brings.

CRACKED FACT

I actually DO have a disgusting brother!

- Ditz

He puts his undies on his hair,

And dances like he doesn't care

It wouldn't be so bad, I fear

But he does it when my friends are here!

Even when they see that sight

My friends say nothing – they're polite

My brother makes me want to hurl

Why couldn't he have been a girl?

SPOT THE DIFFERENCE

BEGINNER

Circle stuff on Bum 1 that's missing from Bum 2:

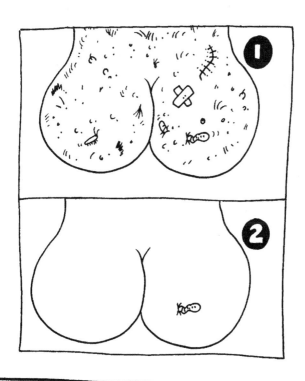

SPOT THE DIFFERENCE

BETTER THAN BEGINNER BUT NOT QUITE EXPERT

Circle stuff on Bum 1 that's missing from Bum 2:

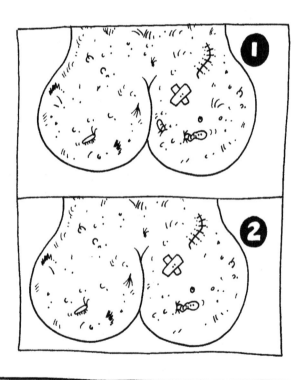

SPOT THE DIFFERENCE

EXPERT

Circle stuff on Bum 1 that's missing from Bum 2:

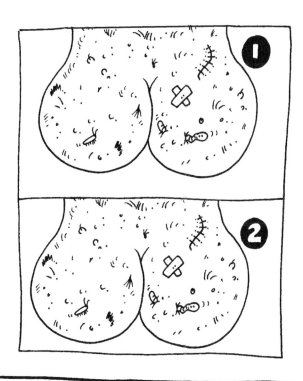

Blaming The Dog

Hey! G'day! My name is Ray

And I'm the Watsons' greyhound

My people feed me every day

And take me to the playground

They let me sleep inside at night

And always take me 'walkies'

There's only one thing I don't like:

They're always telling porkies!

Read the
Cracked Fact!

Every time a Watson farts

A silent, deadly spray

They wait just long enough and then

They call out "oh, no…Ray!"

CRACKED FACT

What are 'porkies'? It's rhyming slang – replacing a word with a phrase that rhymes. Then, to make it more interesting, the phrase gets shortened. So 'porkies' comes from 'pork pies', which is rhyming slang for 'lies'.

– Dawko

Last week, I curled up on the rug

With Gwen, beside the fire

She made a fog, but blamed the dog!

That stinking little liar!

Billy, Ben and Terri, too

They let 'em rip, then blame me

They seem to think 'cause I'm a dog

That farting doesn't shame me

So I get blamed for all of dad's

And even all of mum's

For all the farts they blame on me

I'd need to have three bums!

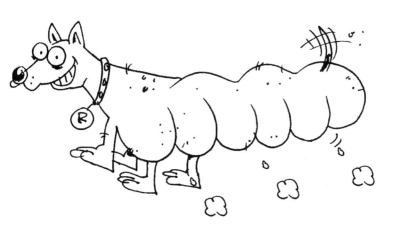

I've started getting my own back

The only way I could

My hearing and my sense of smell

Are really very good

They think they're doing silent farts

But I can hear them loudly

I stand beside the culprit

And I 'bark, bark, bark' quite proudly

I nudge the farter with my nose

I shake and wag my tail

Now every time they blame me

It becomes an epic fail!

Tongue ~~Bum~~ Twisters

Thick stinks stick; thin stinks sink!

A flea's fart afloat flies aft from afar,

a flitting, fleeing flatus

Sloppy poos, ploppy shoes,

     sloppy shoes, ploppy poos

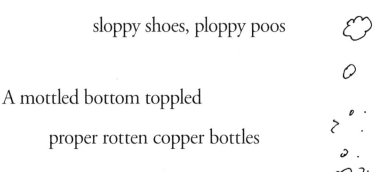

A mottled bottom toppled

     proper rotten copper bottles

In the soiled toilets loitered

     spoiled boys with boisterous poise

Phillip farted feathers farther than

     Phyllis Farmer's father

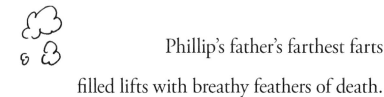

     Phillip's father's farthest farts

filled lifts with breathy feathers of death.

Some snack crumbs down lumberjacks'

     bum cracks come back black lumps

When Friends Fart

When you're out with your friends,

and you're having some fun

Or you're sitting around at the park, in the sun

You want to relax, but before you can start

From somewhere around

comes the smell of a fart

How do you find out

just which smelly friend

Has let something horrid come out of their end?

You do it with rhyme!

Let me show you the way!

These are just some of the things you could say!

Did you just fart, Bart?

You're so smelly, Ellie!

I think I'm dyin', Ryan!

Your bum's quite a blower, Noah!

Oh, you reek, Monique!

I think I'm a goner, Connor!

You're a top farter, Carter!

Did your bum just bark, Mark?

Woof!

MARK

That smells crook, Brooke!

**Is your bum
in flames, James?**

JAMES

Did you let off a bomb, Tom?

Phew! Farts-a-million, Lillian!

Quit that bum-crackery, Zachary!

My nose is bleedin', Eden!

You'd make a grown man spew, Andrew!

That's a smell that I hate, Kate!

That's gross-eph, Joseph!

Did you make that smell, Michelle?

You singed my hair, Claire!

**Your bum
smells like
dead cat, Pat**

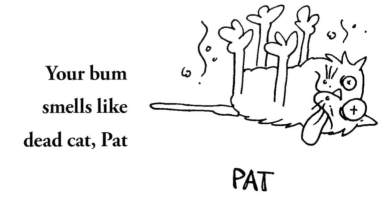

PAT

Your bum's very blowy, Zoe!

Did you melt your crack, Jack?

Stop that fartin', Martin!

I can't wait 'til that's gone, John!

I'm gonna puke, Luke!

Take a wind break, Jake!

You'll start a riot, Wyatt!

Argh! I'm cryin', Brian!

MATTHEW

**You'd make
a cat spew,
Matthew!**

That smell wrecks us, Alexis!

That's making me sick, Dominic!

Was that an earth tremor, Emma?

EMMA

Yuck!
That's gnarly,
Carly!

Don't do that again, Ben!

It's time you were goin', Owen!

Is your bum spillin', Dylan?

You're all that I'm smellin', Helen.

That's not very nice, Bryce!

When are you leavin', Steven?

Better check you didn't poo, Sue!

I think you killed her, Matilda!

That could be diarrhoea, Mia.

Your butt's obscene, Geraldine.

That was a real smeller, Ella!

Did you roll in poo, Drew?

Just shoot me in the head, Ned!

Are you on fire, Isaiah?

That was pretty grim, Kim!

**Did you rip your
dacks, Max?**

Max

That's making
me sick, Rick!

Your bum needs to go, Jo!

That brings a tear to my eye, Guy!

That sprayed me on the chin, Finn!

Cassie

You're outrageously gassy, Cassie.

What's that smell, Narelle?

Was that you, Hugh?

You smell like curried egg, Greg!

Find a toilet in a hurry, Murray!

That smells like a drain, Jane!

That smells like rotten cheese, Louise!

Did you just fill your pants, Lance?

That was a sprayer, Freya!

That smell's from beyond the grave, Dave.

Agh! I'm having fits, Ditz!

Where did my cork go, Dawko?

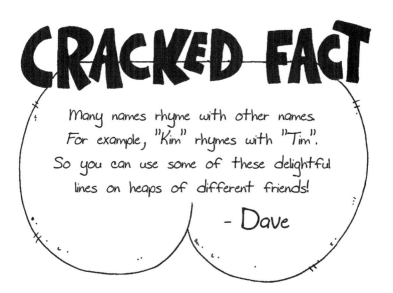

CRACKED FACT

Many names rhyme with other names.
For example, "Kim" rhymes with "Tim".
So you can use some of these delightful
lines on heaps of different friends!

- Dave

112

MAKE YOUR OWN BUTT-MASK

① Sit here.

② Trace your Bum.

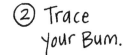

③ Draw on eyes and tie it to your face.

Life of Your Underpants

Have you ever considered your underpants?

And what you do to them when you dance?

They need to stretch this way and that

And be flexible when you fall down flat

What about when you do the splits?

And they have to stretch across your bits

Do they disappear right up your crack?

I really hope you get them back!

Do you think about the wear and tear?

Stretched undies are too much to bear

They fall down easily you see

How do I know?

'Cause it's happened to me!

WHOSE BUM-KITE?

Follow the strings to see who owns each of the spectacular Bum-kites!

THE EVOLUTION OF THE BUM

(One Gazillion BC)

(500,000 B.C.)

(35,000 BC)

(30,000 BC)

(1950 AD)

(21st century)

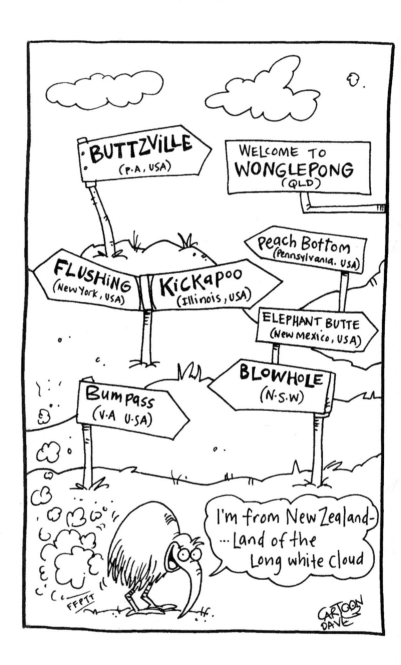

The Boy with the Sideways Bum

There was a boy called Mickey Brown

Whose bum crack didn't go up-down

    This little fact was hard to hide:

His bum was cracked from side-to-side

But Mickey's sideways double bubble

Wasn't really too much trouble

    It wasn't good, it wasn't bad

It was the only bum he had

Of course, he sort of had to cheat

To fit it on the toilet seat

He'd curl up sideways, in a heap

Sometimes he'd even fall asleep!

So okay, he was fine to poo

But some things he found hard to do

Can you think just what it was like

For him to ride a normal bike?

It wasn't long before he found

He had to turn the seat around

A bike seat's hard to sit astride

When your bum crack is on its side

If someone put him in a mood

His bum was great for being rude

When Mickey felt like showing scorn

He'd just bend down, and let it yawn!

And you might think his bum was cursed

But Mickey's bum was not the worst

His brother's bum took out that crown

His brother's bum was upside down!

COOKING WITH BUMS

BUM PIE

This family favourite will have them begging for more!

INGREDIENTS
- 1 BUM
- 1 PIE

METHOD

Combine all Ingredients
Serve hot!

Tastes great with a handful of steamy-fresh cow-poo!

JOIN THE BOTS

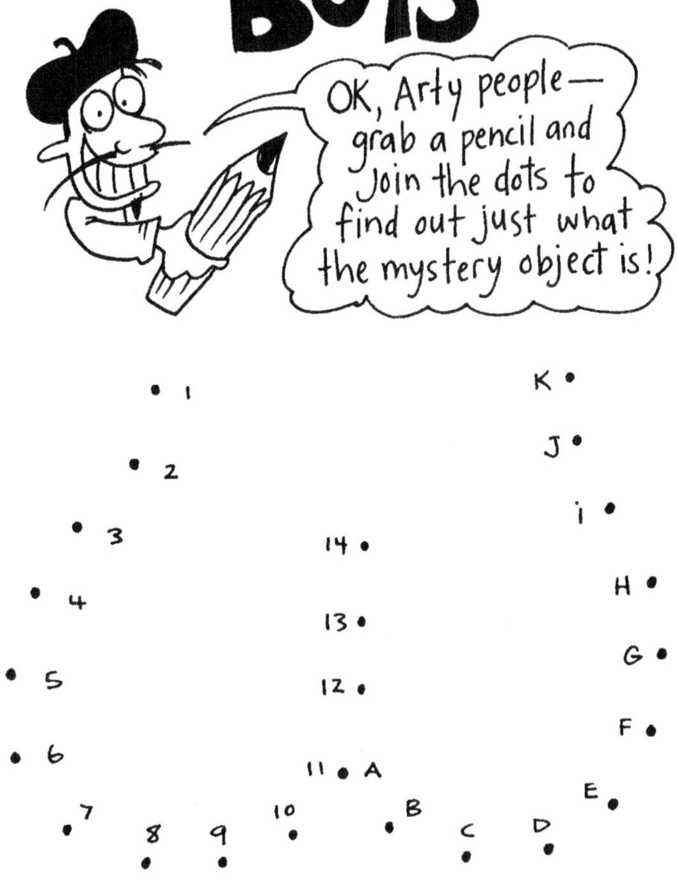

Bumericks

There once was a young girl called Lizzie

Whose bum was remarkably busy

Her poo, she would coil it

Down into the toilet

The smell made her family dizzy!

There once was a young man named Scott

Whose bottom would burp quite a lot

So one day he tried

To keep his farts inside

But they went off just like a gunshot

A lady named Joy, so it's said

Was playing the flute in her shed

When she blew a high note

The air in her throat

Came out of her bottom instead

A lovely young lady named Lauren,

Who was wary of food that was foreign

Ate haggis one day

Then she farted away

And blew off a Scottish man's sporran!

There once was a young boy named Matt

Whose bum made a sound like a cat

It purred and meyowed

(It was really quite loud)

But you had to watch out when it spat!

Young Lewis, on Saturday night

Rode his bike with his undies too tight

When he had a stack

They went up his crack

Young Lewis did get such a fright!

OK... How many words can you make from the letters in the word **BUM**?

List your results below
(Remember—you can only use each letter once)

2 Letter Words:
(2 points each)

——— ———
——— ———
——— ———
———

3 Letter Words:
(5 points each)

——— ———
——— ———
——— ———
——— ———

4 Letter Words:
(3 billion points each)

——— ———
——— ———
——— ———

Wow! So how did you do?
Write your total score here →

Disgusting Brother III:
Captain Knicker-Flicker

My brother's a disgusting boy,

Annoying me gives him such joy

His smelliness is bad enough...

But he's always doing stupid stuff

He grabs the undies off the line

Mum's and dad's and his and mine

Sometimes he grabs them from the hamper

(Some are dry, but some are damper)

He goes up to our big front deck

(And when he does, I just say "heck")

He holds those undies by one side

And twirls them 'round his head with pride

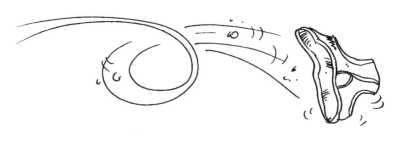

And then he lets those undies go

It's more a flick, it's not a throw

Those undies fly, those undies spin

Those undies make my brother grin

He gets them spinning good and proper

"Look!" he yells. "Just like a chopper!"

Then he says, with quite a snicker

"Call me Captain Knicker-Flicker!"

He does it nearly every day

I never quite know what to say

My brother makes me want to hurl

Why couldn't he have been a girl?

CRACKED FACT

When I was 10, I actually WAS Captain Knicker-Flicker! I did it every day. I even did it at the clothes shops....until the time a salesman caught me in the act!

- Dawko

GREETINGS FROM

Guess The Thing Where The Poem Is Written In The Shape Of The Thing That It's Written About

It makes a sound, it makes a smell, it can not climb a tree... It's nice and round, so who can tell just what this thing might be?

Write your answer here,_____

here_____

or here_____   but **NOT** here!_____

BUM AFRO

MOHAWK of BUTT

BUM HAIRSTYLES

BUTT-MULLET

BOTTOM DREADS

BUM-BUN

YOUR TURN

The Girl
with the Golden Bum

Her face was packed with pus-filled zits

Her teeth all caked in mould,

    Her bloodshot eyes they squirted slime

But her bum was solid gold

    That golden-bottomed girlie

        Was in every way awful

She smelled like rotten duck guts

    And her breath could kill a bull

But her one redeeming asset

(that was passed down from her Mum)

Was that every time she squatted

Dollar coins fell out her bum

THE ADVENTURES OF BUM-PERSON

DRAW
'BUM PERSON'!

① Start with a line...

② add a '?' shape...

③ ..and a backwards one..

④ Now for the eyes...

⑤ End with his chin + mouth!

Butt pimples

Now it's your turn

Floaters and Sinkers

Sitting on the toilet

Every single day

I make sure that I check my poo

To see that it's okay

Did you realise that your poo

Does more than sit and stink?

Depending on your diet

Poo will either float or sink

If you drop a floater

Then it means you're eating junk

You'll very likely find your poo

Is smelly as a skunk!

Look Mum —
a FLOATER!

But if you lay a sinker

Then it means you're eating well

Vegies, fruit and fibre

Make a healthy, pooey smell!

So think about your tucker

and check your poo each day

A sinking poo's a happy poo -

That's all I have to say!

Guess The Thing Where The Poem Is Written In The Shape Of The Thing That It's Written About – Number Two

They're sometimes made of cotton, and they hug your little bo, what are these things that catch your farts? Oh, who can tell me what?

Don't fail to make sure not to forget to remember not to write something that's not your answer not in any other place than not here:

_____

BUM FIND-A-WORD

Try to find all the words from the list in the big bunch of squares below. Words can run forwards, backwards, up, down, and diagonally. Ready? Go!!

My Poo Haiku...
Great Big Number Two

I did a big poo

It landed in the toilet

My bottom got wet

BOTTOM STUFF

Match-up the pictures to their descriptions...

Bottom Drawer ☐　　Bell Bottoms ☐
Bottom Feeder ☐　　Bottom Dollar ☐
Rock Bottom ☐　　　To hit Bottom ☐
Bottom of the ☐　　Some guy
Barrel　　　　　　　wearing a fish hat ☐

The Girl with No Bum

She had a bum

It went away

Where it went

It didn't say

So now she stands

A great big frown

That bumless girl

She can't sit down

BUM FOOD

It's true— food can look like a bum! Don't believe me? Just have a look at these

2× blobs of mashed potato

2× big spoonfuls of ice-cream

2× cupcakes awkwardly shoved together

A pair of Rockmelons

A double-yolked fried egg

Nursery Crhymes

Little Jack Horner

Sat in the corner,

Eating a Brussels sprout

He lifted one cheek

He made his bum squeak

And a terrible smell came out

Jack be nimble

Jack be quick

Jack jump over

The candlestick

Georgie Porgie cabbage and tarts

Scared the girls with all his farts

When the boys came out to play

Georgie blew them all away

One, two, drop a fat poo

Three, four, do a bit more

Five, six, smelly brown bricks

Seven, eight, that's quite a weight

Nine, ten, do it again!

Letters of the Alphabutt

Alimentary Canal: That's the tube inside our bodies that connects our mouths to our bums. Luckily, there's a lot of stuff in between, otherwise when you burped, it might taste like fart!

Buttocks: A properly polite name for your bum cheeks.

Constipation: When your poo gets too hard and dry to come out.

Diarrhoea (die-a-REE-ah): When your poo gets too soft and wet to stay in!

Excrement: A really fancy way to say "poo". Try saying it next time you have to go and back one out! Maybe when you get up from the breakfast table and your mum asks where you're going...you can just say "Mother dear, I feel an urgent need to expel my excessive excrement."

Faeces (FEE-seez): Guess what? It's poo again!

Gluteal Muscles (GLOO-tee-al): These are the different muscles that make up your bum. There are three types of gluteal muscles: *gluteus minimus* (smallest), *gluteus medius* (middle-sized) and *gluteus maximus*, which is not just the biggest muscle of your bum...it's the biggest muscle in your entire body!

Hydrogen: Hydrogen is a gas that makes up as much as half of every fart you do. It's flammable too, so make sure not to fart around a birthday cake!

Ignite: To catch fire...which is what your fart will do if you're too close to a birthday cake.

Jalapeño (ha-la-PEN-yo): A very hot chilli pepper which is used in a lot of Mexican food. It's very hot when it enters your Alimentary Canal...but it's even hotter when it comes out the other end!

Keister (KEY-stir): Another name for your bum. This is a slang word that comes from the United States of America.

Lavatory: A very posh name for a dunny.

Malawi (mah-LAH-wee): A small country in Africa where they tried to outlaw farting in public. How many of your friends would go to prison if public farting was a crime?

Noxious (NOCK-shess): Unpleasant, poisonous or dangerous. This word is perfect to describe the smell of your farts!

Odoriferous (oh-der-IF-er-ess): To give off a smell, usually very bad. Can you think of any part of your body which might be odoriferous? Maybe somewhere in the area between your back and your legs? You know – it rhymes with gum...

Puerile (**PYOO-rile**): Childish or immature. The sorts of thing that your teachers and parents don't like you saying. So basically this whole book!

Quoit (**koit**): A lovely Australian slang name for – you guessed it – your bum!

Roughage (**RUFF-idge**): Stuff you can eat but can't digest, which helps push your food through your guts. So it's like a turbo-charger for your poo engine.

Scat: The poo of an animal, especially a meat-eater. So next time your mate's annoying you, don't yell "scat!"...just yell "POO!"

Toxicity (tock-SISS-i-tee): "Toxic" means "poisonous". So toxicity measures how poisonous something is. I bet your dad's bum would have a very high toxicity!

Upwind: If the wind blows past you before it reaches your mate, then that means you're upwind from him. And that's exactly where you want to be when he farts!

Void: This word can mean an empty space, and it can also mean the act of emptying something. So when you drop a load, you void your bum...and it becomes a void!

Wasabi (wa-SAH-bee): This is one of the most awesome bum-related things on the planet! Wasabi is a plant, and it's from the same family as cabbage and brussels sprouts. The root of the wasabi plant is very hot and spicy. So it's a double-whammy bum buster! It makes you fart, and it burns you on the way out! That's so cool! Or maybe it's really hot!

Xylitol (ZY-li-toll): An artificial sweetener that people use instead of sugar. But for some people, if they eat too much of it, they get diarrhoea and flatulence. If you can't remember what those are, it's runny bum and farting!

Yucky: What poo is. I mean, it really is gross. Hey, did you know that only 1 out of every 5 boys washes his hands after using the toilet? That means 4 out of 5 boys **DO NOT** wash their hands! Now **that's** yucky! So if you're in a group of 5 boys, and you know that **YOU** wash your hands, then the chances are that none of your mates do. So give yourself a high-five... but not your friends!

Zephyr (ZEFF-ur): This means a gentle wind...so it's nothing like those violent storms of mucky air that come shooting from your bum.

I Think I Still Hate Reading...Maybe

That's right. I admit it. It's not just a rumour
I don't like to read, but I love toilet humour
        Bottoms and undies and farting and poo
Who would read that book?
            Well, I would! That's who!

I'd read it from cover to cover, and then
        I'd turn it back over and read it again!
Lots of fun poems and heaps of great pictures…

Hey, maybe I'll check out
            those wizards and witches.

Keep your eyes peeled for more
bum madness coming very soon!
"Fart Jokes For Smelly Kids!" is on the way!

About The Authors

Dawko

A fellow named Dawko, I hear

Was known for his loud stinky rear

Make sure that you're not

Up too close to his bot

Or you just might not hear for a year

You can contact
Dawko via email at:
dawko@thebumbook.com.au

Ditz

I know of a lady called Ditz

Who farts every time that she sits

At parties when there's

Games of musical chairs

It sounds like a flatulent blitz!

Check out our website!
www.thebumbook.com.au

Like us on Facebook!
**www.facebook.com/pages/
The-Bum-Book/100964553386846**

Cartoon Dave

There once was a fellow called Dave

Who didn't know how to behave

The noise from his bum

Scared his dad and his mum

So they sent him to live in a cave

You can contact Dave via email at: **dave@cartoondave.com**
or check out his website: **www.cartoondave.com**

This book was proudly brought to you by

BUM iN A CAN

NOW EVEN MORE TOXIC!!

- Headache?
- Stressed?
- Sore Pancreas?
- Flat Tyre?
- Missing Cat?
- Annoying Sister?
- Pants too Loose?
- Pants too Tight?
- Mucus Overload?
- Can-Opener Broken?
- Lost Your Keys?
- Too much Homework?

If in Doubt—
Squirt one Out!

2 TONNES OF PROTEIN iN EVERY CAN

Available at all leading defartment stores

Printed in Great Britain
by Amazon

82294497R00102